# VOICES OF

*Recovery*

# WORKBOOK

ISBN 978-1-889681-39-9


Overeaters Anonymous®, Inc.
6075 Zenith Court NE
Rio Rancho, New Mexico 87144-6424  USA
Mail Address: PO Box 44020
Rio Rancho, NM 87174-4020 USA
Tel: 505-891-2664
www.oa.org

# TABLE OF CONTENTS

# INTRODUCTION

This workbook provides thought-provoking questions for each of the daily readings in *Voices of Recovery*. When answering these questions, it will be helpful to refer to either a printed copy or an e-reader copy of *Voices of Recovery*.

# JANUARY

**1**    Have I become honest with myself about my compulsive eating?
Can I list the behaviors I know in my heart are problems for me?

_____

_____

_____

_____

_____

_____

_____

_____

_____

_____

**2**    Recovery is a process, not an event. It involves actions on the Steps, tools,
and Traditions. What actions am I taking toward my recovery?

_____

_____

_____

_____

_____

_____

_____

_____

_____

**3** How will I stay or become abstinent today?

_____

_____

_____

_____

_____

_____

_____

_____

_____

_____

_____

_____

**4** What troubling things that I cannot change do I need to accept?

_____

_____

_____

_____

_____

_____

_____

_____

_____

_____

_____

**5**

A program saying is, "Leave the judging of others to God and keep my eyes on my own path." How am I doing on that in the OA rooms and in other parts of my life?

_____

_____

_____

_____

_____

_____

_____

_____

_____

_____

_____

_____

**6**

What can I be doing that I should not expect God to do for me?

_____

_____

_____

_____

_____

_____

_____

_____

_____

_____

_____

_____

_____

**7** An OA expression says, "No problem exists that eating cannot make worse!" What actions, instead of eating, can I take to address my problems?

_____
_____
_____
_____
_____
_____
_____
_____
_____
_____
_____
_____

**8** How would I describe my recovery tapestry? What are the program threads I've used to weave it?

_____
_____
_____
_____
_____
_____
_____
_____
_____
_____
_____
_____

**9**    Is there something scary in my life that I need to deal with? How can I face this with my Higher Power's help?

_____

_____

_____

_____

_____

_____

_____

_____

_____

_____

**10**    In what ways am I willing to do what I need to do physically, emotionally, and spiritually to become abstinent or to maintain my abstinence?

_____

_____

_____

_____

_____

_____

_____

_____

_____

_____

**11**    How do I spend time each day communicating with my Higher Power?

_____

_____

_____

_____

_____

_____

_____

_____

_____

_____

**12**    The future is nothing more than a slow unfolding of "todays." Is my brain engaged in today, or is it encumbered by yesterday's regrets or tomorrow's fears? What examples can I give?

_____

_____

_____

_____

_____

_____

_____

_____

_____

**13** Do I judge and compare by putting others and myself on an imaginary ladder of good or bad, fat or thin, abstinent or not abstinent, or whatever other comparison I wish to make? What are some examples? Is that humility?

_____

_____

_____

_____

_____

_____

_____

_____

_____

_____

_____

_____

**14** Food is not love, security, acceptance, friendship, support, or God. It's simply nourishment for the body. How can I separate "head" hunger from "body" hunger? Do I have hunger of the spirit?

_____

_____

_____

_____

_____

_____

_____

_____

_____

_____

_____

**15** Am I taking the actions that the program promises will lead me to freedom? What are they?

_____

_____

_____

_____

_____

_____

_____

_____

_____

_____

**16** What am I doing to make sure my life is the message I want it to be for newcomers, my family, and everyone I meet?

_____

_____

_____

_____

_____

_____

_____

_____

_____

**17** How am I applying the principles of the Steps and Traditions to my daily life?

_____

_____

_____

_____

_____

_____

_____

_____

_____

_____

_____

**18** Understanding how program works isn't necessary for it to work. Whether or not I understand, how am I taking the suggested actions to support my recovery?

_____

_____

_____

_____

_____

_____

_____

_____

_____

_____

**19**    How am I reaching out to others for help, guidance, or support?

_____

_____

_____

_____

_____

_____

_____

_____

_____

_____

**20**    Am I dealing with today, or am I wasting energy regretting the past or worrying about tomorrow? What are some examples?

_____

_____

_____

_____

_____

_____

_____

_____

_____

_____

**21**  How strong is my connection with my Higher Power?  How can I increase it?

_____

_____

_____

_____

_____

_____

_____

_____

_____

**22**  Do I "Live and let live"?  If not, what is my solution, and is it working for me?

_____

_____

_____

_____

_____

_____

_____

_____

_____

**23**   Are my will and life aligned with the quiet voice within?

_____

_____

_____

_____

_____

_____

_____

_____

_____

_____

**24**   The literature spells out the instructions. Am I following all the instructions, part of the instructions, or trying to do it my way?

_____

_____

_____

_____

_____

_____

_____

_____

_____

_____

**25**   Do I contact other OA members every day? If not, why not?

**26**   Getting out of my own way is not so easy. How am I able to do that?

**27** A reason must exist for why so many members with long-term recovery say abstinence is the most important thing in their lives. Is abstinence the most important thing in my life? How do I explain my answer?

_____

_____

_____

_____

_____

_____

_____

_____

_____

_____

_____

**28** I can't know how my thinking and life may change when I surrender to and work the program. How open is my mind to the new?

_____

_____

_____

_____

_____

_____

_____

_____

_____

_____

**29**  What is the value of having a clearly defined plan of eating, including a list of foods that may be harmful to me?

_____

_____

_____

_____

_____

_____

_____

_____

_____

_____

_____

**30**  A simple definition of insanity is "unsound reasoning and judgment." Where has my reasoning and judgment been unsound around food?

_____

_____

_____

_____

_____

_____

_____

_____

_____

_____

_____

**31** Our Twelve-Step program can arrest the disease, not cure it. My propensity to turn to food, because I have the disease, will always be there. What does this mean for my life?

_____

_____

_____

_____

_____

_____

_____

_____

_____

_____

_____

_____

_____

_____

_____

_____

_____

_____

_____

_____

_____

_____

_____

_____

_____

_____

_____

_____

# FEBRUARY

**1**

Do I believe Higher Power will give me a way to live sanely today if I'm willing to give HP my eating for these 24 hours? What might this look like?

_____
_____
_____
_____
_____
_____
_____
_____
_____
_____

**2**

Even if I've never practiced meditation, am I willing to give it a try today? Can I close my eyes, breathe and let my concept of a loving God envelop me?  What does that feel like?

_____
_____
_____
_____
_____
_____
_____
_____
_____

**3**   What actions, however small, can I take that might change my thinking about difficult situations facing me today? Where will HP be in these actions?

_____

_____

_____

_____

_____

_____

_____

_____

_____

_____

_____

**4**   For today, am I willing to not eat compulsively, no matter what? What tools can I use to help me?

_____

_____

_____

_____

_____

_____

_____

_____

_____

**5**

Does more than one way exist to do the things before me?
Putting self aside, how might the choice I make affect other people?

_____

_____

_____

_____

_____

_____

_____

_____

_____

_____

_____

**6**

How can I plan a way to defuse thoughts—real or imagined—of
food-related pleasures?

_____

_____

_____

_____

_____

_____

_____

_____

_____

_____

_____

**7** Am I willing to let God come between my food and me, so food cannot come between God and me? What examples can I give of doing this?

_____
_____
_____
_____
_____
_____
_____
_____
_____
_____
_____
_____

**8** Us? Am I convinced I belong in OA, or am I still secretly keeping "me" separate from "them"? What am I capable of giving if I completely join our Fellowship?

_____
_____
_____
_____
_____
_____
_____
_____
_____
_____
_____
_____

**9**    Abnormal tendencies, self-will, ego and denial—am I honestly using a daily inventory to keep from eroding my recovery? What does that entail?

_____

_____

_____

_____

_____

_____

_____

_____

_____

_____

_____

_____

**10**    Do fear and faith play tug o' war in my life today? I no longer have to depend on my own unsteady willpower, but how often am I still doing so?

_____

_____

_____

_____

_____

_____

_____

_____

_____

_____

_____

**11** Do I remember what life was like before OA? Do I believe I can change my tomorrows by keeping today free from resentment, guilt and fear? How can I do that?

_____

_____

_____

_____

_____

_____

_____

_____

_____

_____

_____

_____

**12** How can I take action against my isolation today? Am I willing to go to a meeting or reach out to another OA member to remind myself I am no longer alone?

_____

_____

_____

_____

_____

_____

_____

_____

_____

_____

_____

**13** Has food been a god to me? In what ways have I given food power over my life?

_____

_____

_____

_____

_____

_____

_____

_____

_____

_____

_____

_____

**14** Do I try to practice the program principles in all my affairs? Describe my attitude toward my daily reprieve based on the maintenance of my spiritual condition.

_____

_____

_____

_____

_____

_____

_____

_____

_____

_____

_____

**15**    Is my need for an external greater power undeniable, or do I still harbor illusions of self-sufficiency? When and how have I surrendered by taking Steps One, Two and Three?

_____

_____

_____

_____

_____

_____

_____

_____

_____

_____

_____

**16**    Am I convinced that the scale is not my Higher Power? Am I willing to work the entire OA program so I can achieve spiritual, emotional, and physical recovery? How?

_____

_____

_____

_____

_____

_____

_____

_____

_____

_____

**17**  Is my conception of my Higher Power a loving one? How do I experience this love?

_____

_____

_____

_____

_____

_____

_____

_____

_____

_____

**18**  When it comes to character defects, do I believe I have real humility? How would I describe it?

_____

_____

_____

_____

_____

_____

_____

_____

_____

_____

**19** If *I* am the OA message, *what* message am I carrying today?

_____

_____

_____

_____

_____

_____

_____

_____

_____

_____

_____

**20** Where am I today on the self-love meter? How am I reaching out to others in love?

_____

_____

_____

_____

_____

_____

_____

_____

_____

_____

_____

**21** How has applying the OA principles to conflicts helped me identify and overcome knee-jerk reactions?

_____

_____

_____

_____

_____

_____

_____

_____

_____

_____

_____

_____

**22** Do I sometimes suffer from "tiny God syndrome"? How big is my Higher Power?

_____

_____

_____

_____

_____

_____

_____

_____

_____

_____

_____

**23**  What does being "hungry for a principle-based life" mean to me?

_____

_____

_____

_____

_____

_____

_____

_____

_____

_____

_____

**24**  Do I still harbor illusions about being "good" and being "taken care of"? How have I applied the Steps to these illusions? What does it mean to be fully self-supporting?

_____

_____

_____

_____

_____

_____

_____

_____

_____

_____

**25** Am I choosing to use the Steps and tools when the urge to eat compulsively hits me? How do I explain my answer?

_____

_____

_____

_____

_____

_____

_____

_____

_____

_____

_____

**26** Has my concept of HP changed with program? How would I describe my Higher Power today?

_____

_____

_____

_____

_____

_____

_____

_____

_____

_____

**27** How has participating in the group conscience helped me learn to accept different points of view in areas outside OA?

_____

_____

_____

_____

_____

_____

_____

_____

_____

_____

_____

_____

**28** Do I believe the secret of success lies in surrender? How would I explain real humility to a newcomer?

_____

_____

_____

_____

_____

_____

_____

_____

_____

_____

_____

What gifts can I bring to my OA friends and family? Am I doing so and how?

_____

_____

_____

_____

_____

_____

_____

_____

_____

_____

_____

_____

_____

_____

_____

_____

_____

_____

_____

_____

_____

_____

_____

_____

_____

# MARCH

**1**

When have I allowed my new Higher Power to flow in and help me make a good choice? What were the results?

_____

_____

_____

_____

_____

_____

_____

_____

_____

_____

_____

**2**

When have I simply had faith that my Higher Power would resolve a problem? Was the issue resolved?

_____

_____

_____

_____

_____

_____

_____

_____

_____

**3**   When has a simple outreach phone call changed the shape of my day?

_____

_____

_____

_____

_____

_____

_____

_____

_____

_____

_____

_____

**4**   How do I describe my Higher Power?

_____

_____

_____

_____

_____

_____

_____

_____

_____

_____

**5** When have I put something or someone else in my Higher Power's place, and what emotions and outcome resulted?

_____

_____

_____

_____

_____

_____

_____

_____

_____

_____

_____

_____

**6** What can I do to carry the message to suffering compulsive eaters? Am I willing?

_____

_____

_____

_____

_____

_____

_____

_____

_____

_____

_____

_____

**7**  When have I asked God for willingness and directions? How did things turn out?

_____

_____

_____

_____

_____

_____

_____

_____

_____

_____

**8**  What are the details of a recent amends that involved changing my behavior? Have I been able to sustain the changes I committed to when I made the amends?

_____

_____

_____

_____

_____

_____

_____

_____

_____

**9**  What is my definition of compulsiveness? What activities lead me to compulsive behavior?

_____

_____

_____

_____

_____

_____

_____

_____

_____

_____

**10**  When was the last time I took a detour on my road to recovery? What led me back?

_____

_____

_____

_____

_____

_____

_____

_____

_____

_____

**11** How did I feel about my compulsive eating before program? How have those feelings changed since working the Steps?

_____

_____

_____

_____

_____

_____

_____

_____

_____

**12** Do I believe weight loss is a side effect of working the OA program? Do I still harbor a diet mentality? What are some examples?

_____

_____

_____

_____

_____

_____

_____

_____

_____

**13**    When did I last experience significant hurt and pain? What happened? What program Steps or tools did I use during that time?

_____

_____

_____

_____

_____

_____

_____

_____

_____

_____

_____

**14**    What am I doing to recover? Is it enough? What am I willing to do?

_____

_____

_____

_____

_____

_____

_____

_____

_____

_____

_____

**15**     What are some of the gifts God has given me since joining OA?

_____

_____

_____

_____

_____

_____

_____

_____

_____

_____

_____

_____

**16**     Can I describe a situation where I recognized a Higher Power was working in my life?

_____

_____

_____

_____

_____

_____

_____

_____

_____

_____

**17**    What did I lose to this disease prior to OA? Have I regained what I lost?

_____

_____

_____

_____

_____

_____

_____

_____

_____

_____

_____

**18**    Am I honest with my group about my struggles, or do I try to appear "fine"? What would be an example of this?

_____

_____

_____

_____

_____

_____

_____

_____

_____

_____

_____

**19** What program-suggested behaviors have I "practiced"? Have they become easier? What are some examples?

_____

_____

_____

_____

_____

_____

_____

_____

_____

_____

_____

**20** How did I feel after completing Step Five? Did I share those feelings with someone?

_____

_____

_____

_____

_____

_____

_____

_____

_____

_____

_____

**21**    Am I trying to live each day with calm joy, or do I hurry and worry? What are some examples of both?

_____

_____

_____

_____

_____

_____

_____

_____

_____

_____

_____

**22**    What do I think my Higher Power wants for me?

_____

_____

_____

_____

_____

_____

_____

_____

_____

_____

**23** What were my feelings when I first realized I was not alone in this disease? How important is the OA Fellowship to me?

_____

_____

_____

_____

_____

_____

_____

_____

_____

_____

**24** Do I accept that I have an addiction? Am I demonstrating compulsive behaviors other than eating, and if so, what are they?

_____

_____

_____

_____

_____

_____

_____

_____

_____

_____

**25** How have my understanding and vision of my Higher Power changed since coming to OA? Do I put limits on my Higher Power?

_____

_____

_____

_____

_____

_____

_____

_____

_____

_____

**26** When have I remained calm and allowed my Higher Power to be in charge? How did the situation turn out?

_____

_____

_____

_____

_____

_____

_____

_____

_____

_____

**27** "Black or white, all or nothing, good or bad . . ." Do I still view my life and myself through these lenses? How can I better accept others, life and myself?

_____

_____

_____

_____

_____

_____

_____

_____

_____

_____

_____

_____

**28** How have my relationships changed when I have allowed others to see and know the real me?

_____

_____

_____

_____

_____

_____

_____

_____

_____

_____

_____

**29** Am I still being dishonest in any area of my life? In which situations am I dishonest? Am I willing to be honest today?

_____

_____

_____

_____

_____

_____

_____

_____

_____

_____

_____

_____

**30** Do I find excuses to decline service opportunities? Why? What benefits do I believe service brings?

_____

_____

_____

_____

_____

_____

_____

_____

_____

_____

_____

**31**   Am I honest about what I am feeling? If I'm not, why not? How do I express my feelings?

_____
_____
_____
_____
_____
_____
_____
_____
_____
_____
_____
_____
_____
_____
_____
_____
_____
_____
_____
_____
_____
_____
_____
_____
_____
_____

# APRIL

**1**  What fears prevent me from even picking up the pen?

_____

_____

_____

_____

_____

_____

_____

_____

_____

_____

**2**  How do I feel about the repetition required to work my program?

_____

_____

_____

_____

_____

_____

_____

_____

_____

_____

**3** What actions can I take to change from self-willed determination to a desperate desire for Higher Power's help?

_____

_____

_____

_____

_____

_____

_____

_____

_____

_____

_____

_____

**4** What defects of character (judging, condemning, controlling, etc.) prevent me from accepting people just the way they are?

_____

_____

_____

_____

_____

_____

_____

_____

_____

_____

_____

**5**   How did I think HP was going to remove my weight? What made me realize I may also have some work to do to achieve weight loss?

_____
_____
_____
_____
_____
_____
_____
_____
_____
_____
_____

**6**   Do I check in with my Higher Power? How and when do I check?

_____
_____
_____
_____
_____
_____
_____
_____
_____
_____

**7**     Do I act out of ego-driven stubbornness, or do I persevere while surrendering to my Higher Power? What tools can help me see the difference?

_____

_____

_____

_____

_____

_____

_____

_____

_____

_____

_____

_____

**8**     What are the benefits of willingness? Has this gift helped me experience the Twelve-Step principles?

_____

_____

_____

_____

_____

_____

_____

_____

_____

_____

_____

**9**    What do I need to "pack" on this trip toward physical, emotional, and
spiritual recovery?

_____

_____

_____

_____

_____

_____

_____

_____

_____

_____

**10**    What is my primary purpose for being in this program?

_____

_____

_____

_____

_____

_____

_____

_____

_____

**11**   What are some people, events, or ways through which the teacher has come to me when I sought answers?

_____

_____

_____

_____

_____

_____

_____

_____

_____

_____

_____

**12**   Am I still afraid of making mistakes? How has practicing Step Three helped me get past my fears?

_____

_____

_____

_____

_____

_____

_____

_____

_____

_____

**13** Do I still play the comparison game with everyone, or have I achieved a measure of value about myself? Using the gifts of respect, love, gratitude, and humility, can I list the values and talents of which I am now aware?

_____

_____

_____

_____

_____

_____

_____

_____

_____

_____

_____

**14** What footprints have I followed and do I follow them still? What footprints am I leaving?

_____

_____

_____

_____

_____

_____

_____

_____

_____

_____

**15** Do I still have secrets to share? What are they? Do I see a connection between secrets and struggles with abstinence?

_____

_____

_____

_____

_____

_____

_____

_____

_____

_____

_____

**16** When the desire for excess food comes, which tool do I use most often and what are the results after I use it? What other tools could I use in these situations?

_____

_____

_____

_____

_____

_____

_____

_____

_____

_____

_____

**17** How would I describe one of my OA friendships, and how has this relationship enhanced my life?

_____

_____

_____

_____

_____

_____

_____

_____

_____

_____

_____

**18** How does continuing to practice the Steps and their principles give my life purpose and direction?

_____

_____

_____

_____

_____

_____

_____

_____

_____

_____

_____

**19** Can I allow God to take the worry, leaving me to do my footwork just for today? How do I apply the concept of "one day at a time" in my life?

_____

_____

_____

_____

_____

_____

_____

_____

_____

_____

_____

**20** How do I give compassion and encouragement to those struggling within the fellowship?  Does that include me?

_____

_____

_____

_____

_____

_____

_____

_____

_____

_____

**21**  Do I offer help to others in OA? How?

_____

_____

_____

_____

_____

_____

_____

_____

_____

_____

_____


**22**  Does hearing someone share an intimate event at a meeting help me understand that I too can trust someone with my secrets? Do I then feel free to share? What are some examples?

_____

_____

_____

_____

_____

_____

_____

_____

_____

**23** Describe a time when I asked my Higher Power to "feed me." What happens when I don't ask for help with food choices?

_____
_____
_____
_____
_____
_____
_____
_____
_____
_____
_____
_____

**24** When I receive praise and recognition, do I remember to say, "Thank you, God"? What does humility mean to me?

_____
_____
_____
_____
_____
_____
_____
_____
_____
_____
_____

**25**   What excuses do I use to avoid putting my recovery first?

_____

_____

_____

_____

_____

_____

_____

_____

_____

_____

_____

**26**   What event or situation recently called for my patience, and what was the result when I "let go and let God"?

_____

_____

_____

_____

_____

_____

_____

_____

_____

_____

_____

**27** Am I convinced that if I eat over any storm in my life, I will have two problems instead of one? What simple action can I take to remind myself that abstinence is number one?

_____

_____

_____

_____

_____

_____

_____

_____

_____

_____

_____

_____

**28** Do I keep my commitments, striving for honesty and discipline? What is my daily action plan?

_____

_____

_____

_____

_____

_____

_____

_____

_____

_____

_____

**29**  What can separate me from others and feed my isolation? What actions can I take to feel connected today?

_____

_____

_____

_____

_____

_____

_____

_____

_____

_____

_____

**30**  How do I handle anger? Would making a gratitude list help change my thoughts?

_____

_____

_____

_____

_____

_____

_____

_____

_____

_____

_____

# MAY

**1**  Do I accept I have a disease over which willpower is useless? How do I know that? What am I willing to do about it?

_____

_____

_____

_____

_____

_____

_____

_____

_____

_____

**2**  What is my relationship with the God of my understanding?

_____

_____

_____

_____

_____

_____

_____

_____

_____

_____

**3** How am I keeping OA's responsibility pledge: "Always to extend the hand and heart of OA to all who share my compulsion; for this I am responsible"?

_____

_____

_____

_____

_____

_____

_____

_____

_____

_____

_____

**4** What can I do to help members struggling with the program?

_____

_____

_____

_____

_____

_____

_____

_____

_____

_____

**5** Unconditional support can be helpful and constructive, or it can enable unwillingness to take the actions leading to recovery. Where am I on this scale? Am I helping or hindering?

**6** Am I still fighting the disease, or have I achieved the freedom promised in the Twelve Steps? If I'm still fighting, which part of the program am I not working?

I really am so new to this program, this radical way of thinking that I don't feel, for the first time, that I am fighting this disease I have. I know, without a doubt that I am a compulsive overeater. I look forward to the freedoms that were listed in today's. I am in bondage but that will be broken as I get and remain abstinent.

**7**    Am I letting the people in my life be who they are? What examples can I give?

_____

_____

_____

_____

_____

_____

_____

_____

_____

_____

_____

_____

**8**    How do I get myself into, and keep myself in, good spiritual condition?

_____

_____

_____

_____

_____

_____

_____

_____

_____

_____

_____

**9** If I use the principles of the program as an inventory for how I'm living my life, how am I doing?

The principles and how I am doing today - my inventory. Honesty - yes, I am being completely honest today to myself and to others. Hope - I am truly the most hopeful than I have (been) that my desire to compulsively eat will and is being removed. Courage - Definitely this takes a lot of courage but God is absolutely giving me the courage I need to do this. Willingness - yes I am completely willing to do what it takes, listen to suggestions and execute these suggestions. Self-discipline is coming from God, as long as I truly ask for help.

Service - yes want to be of service and will step up as I move along in the program. Today is good, I am embracing all of this as the quality of my life depends upon it. None of this is an option for me today.

**10** "Half measures availed us nothing" (*Alcoholics Anonymous*, 4th ed., p.59). Am I committed to practicing all the Steps and using all the tools? How?

**11** Staying in recovery requires taking daily actions forever. As the slogan says, "When we rest on our oars, we drift downstream." How would I describe my daily actions? Are they enough?

_____

_____

_____

_____

_____

_____

_____

_____

_____

_____

_____

_____

**12** Is perfectionism getting in my way?  How do I celebrate my progress?

_____

_____

_____

_____

_____

_____

_____

_____

_____

_____

_____

**13** Other ways may exist to arrest my food problem, but I know from others that the OA program works. How am I working it?

- I start my morning with an oa meeting, this allows me to read and share the literature.
- I send my food plan to the my sponsor
- I am starting on step 1 again.
- I call my Sponsor and check in daily
- I do want to really try to reach out to others, that is still missing.

**14** There is abstinence, or there is compulsive eating. Abstinence stops the war within and frees me to live fully. Am I willing to do whatever I must to stay abstinent? What examples can I give?

**15** Do I do what is necessary every day to have a relationship with HP? How do I explain my answer?

_____

_____

_____

_____

_____

_____

_____

_____

_____

_____

_____

_____

_____

**16** Does my "yesterday" sometimes crowd out my today? Do I waste today's energy and time tangled up in worry about tomorrow's "what ifs"? What are some examples?

_____

_____

_____

_____

_____

_____

_____

_____

_____

_____

_____

_____

**17** If my commitment or willingness to take the actions is lagging, do I need to revisit the Third Step? What might that bring?

_____
_____
_____
_____
_____
_____
_____
_____
_____
_____
_____
_____

**18** Sometimes, after the Serenity Prayer, we close our meetings by saying, "It works if you work it." That's a promise. Where am I on this promise?

I do believe this 100%. It does work if you work it. So what works? This program to help us to stop our compulsive eating behaviors. The "it" is three fold - body, mind and spirit. Having a food plan and following it is the body. Not snacking between meals or eating after dinner is the body. The mind is reading the literature, attending meetings, working with a sponsor, ask questions and listen to what has worked for others. Spirit entails God for me. I have to trust him and what he has promised me. I have to rely on him and reach out to him in prayer and in thanksgiving - always. Only in working my program with all 3 areas engaged will it work, hence, "it works if you work it"

**19** Indecision, like overeating, can be toxic. How do I seek my HP's guidance and the counsel of trusted others in my decision-making?

---

**20** What does the phrase "Love myself first" mean to me?

love

Love myself is a tough one for me. I had not loved myself fully, ever, yet. Not even today do I fully love myself but I am loving myself more than I had, even as early as two weeks ago. Today I show myself by getting up for early morning meetings. By sending my food plan to my sponsor. By even having a sponsor. I am showing love to myself by NOT dieting! I am showing love to myself by dressing well, by going to the gym

I am showing love to myself - finally!!

**21**  How do I give back the love and acceptance I received when I came to OA?

_____

_____

_____

_____

_____

_____

_____

_____

_____

_____

_____

**22**  Am I using all the help, support and guidance available to me in OA? What are some examples?

_____

_____

_____

_____

_____

_____

_____

_____

_____

**23**    Which foods and eating behaviors cause me problems?

_____

_____

_____

_____

_____

_____

_____

_____

_____

_____

_____

_____

**24**    Decisions, unless followed by action, are meaningless. Working and living Steps Four through Twelve are the fulfillment of the decision made in Step Three. How is my progress?

_____

_____

_____

_____

_____

_____

_____

_____

_____

_____

_____

**25** The busier or more difficult my life, the more I need the program. How do I kick my program into a higher gear in these difficult times?

_____

_____

_____

_____

_____

_____

_____

_____

_____

_____

_____

**26** Sometimes we hear, "Take what you need and leave the rest." If the program isn't working well for me, are some of the things I'm leaving really things I should be taking? What are some examples?

_____

_____

_____

_____

_____

_____

_____

_____

_____

_____

**27** Recovery from my three-fold disease requires change at the physical, emotional, and spiritual levels. More often than not, sustained abstinence is the result of emotional and spiritual fitness. Have I made the necessary changes to my thinking and beliefs? How do I explain my answer?

_____

_____

_____

_____

_____

_____

_____

_____

_____

_____

_____

**28** How am I working and living Step Ten every day? Is my inventory process adequate?

_____

_____

_____

_____

_____

_____

_____

_____

_____

_____

**29**    Am I still resisting the idea of powerlessness? What can I do to reach an unconscious acceptance of my need for help?

---

---

---

---

---

---

---

---

---

---

---

---

---

**30**    What did I gain physically, emotionally, or spiritually from compulsive eating or other self-destructive behaviors? Am I willing to deal with life without those crutches?

---

---

---

---

---

---

---

---

---

---

---

---

**31** The Traditions imply moral principles, including fellowship, equality, acceptance, responsibility, trust, open mindedness, and unity. How am I applying these principles in my life?

_____

_____

_____

_____

_____

_____

_____

_____

_____

_____

_____

_____

_____

_____

_____

_____

_____

_____

_____

_____

_____

_____

_____

# JUNE

**1**  What defects do I notice most in other people? Do I still practice these defects myself? If so, what can I do about it?

---

---

---

---

---

---

---

---

---

---

**2**  What problems do I expect God or other people to solve for me? Am I willing to do my part? How do I accept responsibility for my feelings and actions?

---

---

---

---

---

---

---

---

---

**3**  Am I willing to stop compulsively eating right now, even if I am not yet able to adhere to a "perfect" food plan? What one small thing can I do for my recovery today?

_____

_____

_____

_____

_____

_____

_____

_____

_____

_____

_____

_____

**4**  Am I still trying to do it alone, or have I acknowledged my powerlessness over my character defects? Can I write a prayer asking for help?

_____

_____

_____

_____

_____

_____

_____

_____

_____

_____

_____

**5**    What can I do to be a living message of OA recovery?

_____

_____

_____

_____

_____

_____

_____

_____

_____

_____

**6**    Do I accept others as they are? Am I consciously choosing positive thoughts and decisions?  Is there a connection between my food obsession and my willingness to accept life on life's terms?  What are some examples?

_____

_____

_____

_____

_____

_____

_____

_____

_____

_____

**7** Do I believe and accept that my commitment to abstinence from compulsive eating is the most important thing in my life without exception? How am I committed and consistent in putting abstinence first?

_____

_____

_____

_____

_____

_____

_____

_____

_____

_____

_____

_____

**8** Do I try to clear my mind and focus on God's will? What prayer do I use to ask for the power to carry out God's will? Am I trying to do this regularly throughout each day?

_____

_____

_____

_____

_____

_____

_____

_____

_____

_____

_____

**9**     What excuses do I still use to break my abstinence? How do I plan well? Do I check in with my sponsor before special occasions?

_____

_____

_____

_____

_____

_____

_____

_____

_____

_____

**10**     Do I still feel like I _am_ a mistake when I make a mistake? Do I share my mistakes and feelings with others? What examples can I give?

_____

_____

_____

_____

_____

_____

_____

_____

_____

**11**  Am I careful about my attitude toward anger? Do I let righteous anger take up room in my life? What do I still get out of holding onto anger and resentment?

_____

_____

_____

_____

_____

_____

_____

_____

_____

_____

_____

**12**  What defects do I cling to and what difficulties do they cause me? Am I ready to begin practicing a new way of living?

_____

_____

_____

_____

_____

_____

_____

_____

_____

_____

_____

**13**     What fills me with Sacred Awe?

_____

_____

_____

_____

_____

_____

_____

_____

_____

_____

_____

**14**     What keeps me from giving up control?  In what ways do I still believe my way is the right way?

_____

_____

_____

_____

_____

_____

_____

_____

_____

_____

**15** Do I believe it is possible for me to have the miracle of sanity around food and remain abstinent day after day? Am I willing to give up compulsive eating, one day at a time? Am I honest about my plan of eating? How do I explain my answers?

_____

_____

_____

_____

_____

_____

_____

_____

_____

_____

_____

**16** Am I disciplined about my recovery? Am I still doing what I can get away with or what I want to do? Am I willing to go through the pain, discomfort, and patience that discipline requires? How do I explain my answers?

_____

_____

_____

_____

_____

_____

_____

_____

_____

_____

**17**

When have I enjoyed a period of complete freedom from the obsession with food and the compulsion to overeat? Am I willing to work and live by the Steps to overcome the obsession?

_____

_____

_____

_____

_____

_____

_____

_____

_____

_____

_____

**18**

Am I using the OA tools and listening to my sponsor and others to help me know what changes to make? In what areas are fear, control, self-pity, or self-centeredness still interfering in my life?

_____

_____

_____

_____

_____

_____

_____

_____

_____

_____

**19** Have I examined my past in order to understand myself and let the past go? How am I making an ongoing effort to uncover, discover and discard?

_____

_____

_____

_____

_____

_____

_____

_____

_____

_____

_____

_____

**20** When faced with an important decision, how do I pray about it?

_____

_____

_____

_____

_____

_____

_____

_____

_____

_____

**21**  In what ways can I see my Higher Power at work in my life, giving me guidance? What examples have I experienced of a new course of action or a different solution that must have come from a Higher Power?

_____

_____

_____

_____

_____

_____

_____

_____

_____

_____

_____

_____

**22**  Do I think I might have "arrived" in OA? What is the difference between commencing and graduating?

_____

_____

_____

_____

_____

_____

_____

_____

_____

_____

_____

**23** How are my shortcomings transforming into assets? Can I list the assets into which God might transform my character defects?

_____

_____

_____

_____

_____

_____

_____

_____

_____

_____

_____

**24** What signals about food do I receive that are quite different from those that normal eaters receive? Do I focus on my differences from other OA members rather than on our common disease? In what ways do I still feel isolated, different, or ashamed?

_____

_____

_____

_____

_____

_____

_____

_____

_____

_____

_____

**25**    Am I willing to keep coming back whether abstinent or not? Who are the right people of whom I might ask profound questions, and what are those questions?

_____

_____

_____

_____

_____

_____

_____

_____

_____

_____

_____

**26**    What do I have trouble accepting, and can I "act as if"?

_____

_____

_____

_____

_____

_____

_____

_____

_____

_____

**27** Can I offer hope to others, and can I accept the hope they offer me? In what ways can I help others feel welcome in OA?

_____

_____

_____

_____

_____

_____

_____

_____

_____

_____

_____

**28** In what ways do I delude myself into thinking that, apart from the eating, I am doing fine? How is my Higher Power taking care of me?

_____

_____

_____

_____

_____

_____

_____

_____

_____

_____

**29**    Have I learned an attitude of mercy and forgiveness? Can I let go of the idea of perfection and accept reality, loving people just the way they are? How do I explain my answers?

_____

_____

_____

_____

_____

_____

_____

_____

_____

_____

_____

**30**    Do I still believe in diets and focus on my weight? Can I believe my weight is none of my business and let HP take care of it while I practice abstinence?

_____

_____

_____

_____

_____

_____

_____

_____

_____

_____

# JULY

**1** Do I have an attitude of deference, humility, and trust when taking my character defects to my Higher Power? How do I explain my response?

_____

_____

_____

_____

_____

_____

_____

_____

_____

_____

**2** Do I spend time affirming my value and worth? What can I do through Step Seven to create a nurturing environment within which to grow and heal?

_____

_____

_____

_____

_____

_____

_____

_____

_____

_____

_____

**3** How has humility manifested in my life? Am I able to see where my Higher Power has changed my attitudes?

_____

_____

_____

_____

_____

_____

_____

_____

_____

_____

_____

**4** Have I surrendered my food to my Higher Power? Am I still keeping areas of my life from my Higher Power's grace? Am I still fighting my disease? How do I explain my answers?

_____

_____

_____

_____

_____

_____

_____

_____

_____

**5** Who might benefit if I say the prayer, "Bless 'so and so' and change me"? Do I recognize my need for Higher Power's help even to change myself?

---

---

---

---

---

---

---

---

---

---

**6** Am I still settling for "good" when my Higher Power wants to give me "best"? How am I experiencing the freedom of recovery today?

---

---

---

---

---

---

---

---

---

---

**7** Do I still blame other people or my circumstances for my overeating, choices, feelings, or actions? How do I explain my response?

_____

_____

_____

_____

_____

_____

_____

_____

_____

_____

**8** Do I have peace around my food, or am I still in bondage? Am I willing to practice rigorous honesty so I can recover? How do I explain my answers?

_____

_____

_____

_____

_____

_____

_____

_____

_____

**9**   Do I have a home group meeting? How do I support my home group meeting and the other members who attend?

_____

_____

_____

_____

_____

_____

_____

_____

_____

_____

_____

**10**   Have I considered that taking Step Seven is like applying Steps One and Two to my shortcomings? How would this change the way I practice this Step?

_____

_____

_____

_____

_____

_____

_____

_____

_____

_____

_____

**11** Do I listen in meetings no matter who is speaking? Which of the OA tools can help me learn to listen?

_____

_____

_____

_____

_____

_____

_____

_____

_____

_____

**12** How has perseverance helped me work my program? When I "Keep Coming Back" to my HP, is my Higher Power also reaching out to me?

_____

_____

_____

_____

_____

_____

_____

_____

_____

_____

**13** Have I seen the promise of "We cannot fail to recover" manifest in my life? Do I start each morning in quiet time with my Higher Power? How can I practice trusting my Higher Power today?

_____

_____

_____

_____

_____

_____

_____

_____

_____

_____

**14** Have I established a daily practice of writing? How has writing brought me clarity on an issue or problem?

_____

_____

_____

_____

_____

_____

_____

_____

_____

**15** Is keeping my word a priority today? What choices can I make today to support my commitment to my recovery?

_____

_____

_____

_____

_____

_____

_____

_____

_____

_____

_____

**16** How does my Higher Power speak to me? How can I cultivate my relationship with my Higher Power?

_____

_____

_____

_____

_____

_____

_____

_____

_____

_____

**17**    Have I made time today to improve my conscious contact with my Higher Power? Am I practicing surrender by asking my Higher Power for help? Has the miracle happened for me?

_____

_____

_____

_____

_____

_____

_____

_____

_____

_____

_____

**18**    How has my perspective about the disease changed? How can I cultivate gratitude today?

_____

_____

_____

_____

_____

_____

_____

_____

_____

_____

**19**  Am I willing to ask others for help and listen to their experience?
In what ways am I teachable?

_____

_____

_____

_____

_____

_____

_____

_____

_____

_____

_____

**20**  Am I allowing my feelings about past events to stop me from experiencing
the freedom of today? Can I describe a situation in my life that I can view
through spiritual eyes to gain a new perspective?

_____

_____

_____

_____

_____

_____

_____

_____

_____

_____

**21** Am I still experimenting with eating instead of surrendering?
How have I sought my Higher Power's guidance for my plan of eating?

_____

_____

_____

_____

_____

_____

_____

_____

_____

_____

_____

_____

**22** Am I making choices and taking action so I can go to sleep abstinent?
What are the benefits of continued abstinence?

_____

_____

_____

_____

_____

_____

_____

_____

_____

_____

_____

**23** Have I experienced a new freedom and happiness? What am I willing to give in exchange for freedom? Can I describe the freedom that comes from turning my will and life over to my Higher Power?

_____

_____

_____

_____

_____

_____

_____

_____

_____

**24** Do I believe self-knowledge avails me nothing? Do I still believe I can control my eating? How am I allowing my Higher Power to help me with my eating problem?

_____

_____

_____

_____

_____

_____

_____

_____

_____

**25** Do I accept that I must reach out to my Higher Power for help letting go of self-will? Is my Higher Power meeting my needs? Am I at peace with my Higher Power today?

_____

_____

_____

_____

_____

_____

_____

_____

_____

_____

_____

**26** Am I committed to abstinence today? What am I willing to do to maintain the gift of abstinence? What do I need to remember before I take that first compulsive bite?

_____

_____

_____

_____

_____

_____

_____

_____

_____

_____

**27** What am I trying to "figure out" today? What am I willing to surrender to my Higher Power today?

_____
_____
_____
_____
_____
_____
_____
_____
_____
_____
_____

**28** Do I accept who I am today? Do I like myself? Do I love myself? Am I able to see myself through my Higher Power's eyes? What does that look like?

_____
_____
_____
_____
_____
_____
_____
_____
_____
_____

**29** How would I explain the concept that we have a daily reprieve from compulsive eating? Am I experiencing freedom today? What am I willing to do to maintain my recovery?

_____

_____

_____

_____

_____

_____

_____

_____

_____

_____

_____

**30** How do I listen? Do I listen prayerfully when others are speaking? Can I practice listening today?

_____

_____

_____

_____

_____

_____

_____

_____

_____

_____

**31** What are some good habits I can work on in place of bad habits?
To incorporate these new habits, what might my action plan look like?

# AUGUST

**1** Have I experienced the healing that can occur because I've forgiven an old wrong? How has learning to forgive helped me to see where I've been at fault and clean my side of the street?

_____

_____

_____

_____

_____

_____

_____

_____

_____

**2** If sustained abstinence eludes me, is it because I'm not willing to ask God for help in living within my eating guidelines? Why not?

_____

_____

_____

_____

_____

_____

_____

_____

**3**   If letting go of my top one or two shortcomings would move me so much closer to being who I want to be, what exactly am I getting from each one that causes me to hang on to it?

_____

_____

_____

_____

_____

_____

_____

_____

_____

_____

_____

**4**   Am I holding on to any old, destructive habits? If I have divested myself of any such habits, how has my life changed?

_____

_____

_____

_____

_____

_____

_____

_____

_____

_____

**5** Do I still struggle with a negative self-image, seeing myself as ugly, flawed or unlovable? How can the Steps help me obtain a realistic image of my gifts, my better qualities and myself today?

_____

_____

_____

_____

_____

_____

_____

_____

_____

_____

**6** Has food been a source of comfort and relaxation for me in the past? Do I have the willingness today to surrender my food and let go of fear? What are healthier ways to relax?

_____

_____

_____

_____

_____

_____

_____

_____

_____

**7**    Have I ever experienced food nightmares? What have I learned from them?

_____

_____

_____

_____

_____

_____

_____

_____

_____

_____

**8**    Have I skipped over any Steps? If so, why? Do I believe I'm so unique the Steps do not apply to me?

_____

_____

_____

_____

_____

_____

_____

_____

_____

_____

**9**    Am I incorporating all Twelve Steps into my daily life in a way that makes me an example that the program works?

_____

_____

_____

_____

_____

_____

_____

_____

_____

_____

_____

**10**    When faced with tough decisions, how do I remind myself that I've taken Step Three? After doing so, am I willing to keep my end of the bargain and ask for HP's guidance?

_____

_____

_____

_____

_____

_____

_____

_____

_____

_____

**11**    Am I choosing to allow negativity, resentments, or fear "eat away" at my abstinence today, or will I choose gratitude for another day in recovery? How do I explain my response?

_____

_____

_____

_____

_____

_____

_____

_____

_____

_____

_____

_____

**12**    In what ways am I reaching for more recovery today? I cannot coast for long; what will I do to stretch myself?

_____

_____

_____

_____

_____

_____

_____

_____

_____

_____

_____

**13** Do I have a contented abstinence? If not, how can I use the Fellowship and the Twelve Steps to get off the treadmill of either controlling my food but not enjoying it, or enjoying my food but not controlling it?

_____

_____

_____

_____

_____

_____

_____

_____

_____

_____

_____

**14** What steps can I take today to help me let go of control and just be a vessel of service at meetings, work, and home?

_____

_____

_____

_____

_____

_____

_____

_____

_____

_____

_____

**15** Do I show up at meetings and honestly share my experience, strength, and hope?  Or do I withhold, judge, and look for what I can get rather than what I can give? How do I explain my answers?

_____

_____

_____

_____

_____

_____

_____

_____

_____

_____

_____

_____

**16** Have I noticed my urge to control others is related to my attempts to control my food? Who's in charge today—my HP or me? How do I demonstrate this?

_____

_____

_____

_____

_____

_____

_____

_____

_____

_____

**17** How have I cultivated my belief in a power greater than myself? How has this Higher Power relieved my compulsions around food and eating behaviors?

_____

_____

_____

_____

_____

_____

_____

_____

_____

_____

_____

**18** What rewards have I experienced from my willingness to become vulnerable and speak my truth without censoring?

_____

_____

_____

_____

_____

_____

_____

_____

_____

_____

_____

**19**    How was I kind and courteous to myself today (which includes being abstinent)? How was I kind and courteous toward others?

---
---
---
---
---
---
---
---
---
---
---
---

**20**    Has abstinence helped me to better keep commitments? Am I a more reliable person? If not, how can I put the principles of honesty and perseverance into practice on this shortcoming?

---
---
---
---
---
---
---
---
---
---
---

**21**   When food begins to trouble me, how do I use the tools of writing, prayer, and meditation to uncover any emotional or spiritual problems I am experiencing? Am I willing to reach for a pen instead of a fork when a sudden craving for "a little something" hits me? Why or why not?

_____

_____

_____

_____

_____

_____

_____

_____

_____

_____

_____

**22**   Is criticizing others a way of life for me? Am I able to see my character defects in others and find compassion? How do I explain my responses?

_____

_____

_____

_____

_____

_____

_____

_____

_____

_____

**23** How powerful has hope been in my recovery? How willing am I to offer that same hope to newcomers?

_____

_____

_____

_____

_____

_____

_____

_____

_____

_____

_____

_____

**24** Have I been lying to myself? Am I willing to go to any lengths for the recovery OA offers? If I'm unwilling, am I at least willing to pray for willingness? How do I explain my answers?

_____

_____

_____

_____

_____

_____

_____

_____

_____

_____

_____

**25** Is fear holding me back from full recovery and being fully alive? What can I do today to let go of fear and step into the unknowns of growth?

_____
_____
_____
_____
_____
_____
_____
_____
_____
_____
_____

**26** How have I changed my thinking? Have I let go of a diet mentality and embraced working the Steps and using the tools, which allow me to let HP change me from the inside out?

_____
_____
_____
_____
_____
_____
_____
_____
_____
_____

**27** Do I trust food more than HP? Isn't that what I am doing if I choose to eat instead of pray when I'm faced with adversity, fear, or sadness? What can I do differently?

_____

_____

_____

_____

_____

_____

_____

_____

_____

_____

_____

**28** What lies has my disease sometimes convinced me are true?

_____

_____

_____

_____

_____

_____

_____

_____

_____

_____

**29** Do I love myself? Am I lovable? Am I capable of loving others? Why do I feel this way?

_____

_____

_____

_____

_____

_____

_____

_____

_____

_____

_____

**30** Am I holding onto a problem or worry that I need to turn over to God? What is it?

_____

_____

_____

_____

_____

_____

_____

_____

_____

_____

_____

**31** Have I experienced letting go of certainty and walking into the unknown with HP? What was the outcome?

_____

_____

_____

_____

_____

_____

_____

_____

_____

_____

_____

_____

_____

_____

_____

_____

_____

_____

_____

_____

_____

_____

_____

_____

_____

# S E P T E M B E R

**1** Do I still have Ninth-Step amends to make because I haven't let go of some guilt, shame, or resentment? If so, what can I do to move forward?

_____
_____
_____
_____
_____
_____
_____
_____
_____
_____

**2** What impact did making a specific amends have on my life?

_____
_____
_____
_____
_____
_____
_____
_____
_____
_____

**3**    What was a situation where fear kept me stuck? What actions did I take or could have taken to move forward?

_____
_____
_____
_____
_____
_____
_____
_____
_____
_____
_____
_____

**4**    How would I describe my relationship with my Higher Power?

_____
_____
_____
_____
_____
_____
_____
_____
_____
_____
_____

**5**    Do I accept people in my life as they are? What expectations do I place on people, and do those expectations cause me resentments when they are not met? How do I explain my response?

_____

_____

_____

_____

_____

_____

_____

_____

_____

_____

_____

**6**    When has my Higher Power worked "for, through and in me"? Am I open to the awareness of HP in my life?

_____

_____

_____

_____

_____

_____

_____

_____

_____

_____

_____

**7** What are some shortcomings that may have served me well in the past but now may be causing problems in my life?

_____

_____

_____

_____

_____

_____

_____

_____

_____

_____

_____

**8** Am I honestly self-supporting in OA? Do I take my share of responsibility for keeping OA alive? If so, how?

_____

_____

_____

_____

_____

_____

_____

_____

_____

_____

**9**   What was a situation where I prayed for guidance, and how did I receive an answer?

_____
_____
_____
_____
_____
_____
_____
_____
_____
_____
_____
_____

**10**   What emotions still trigger my desire to eat? What tools do I or could I use in place of picking up the food?

_____
_____
_____
_____
_____
_____
_____
_____
_____
_____
_____

**11**   When and how did I realize God would help me with compulsive eating?

_____

_____

_____

_____

_____

_____

_____

_____

_____

_____

**12**   Am I aware of my continuing powerlessness over food? Do I remember the insanity, or have I become complacent? What examples can I give?

_____

_____

_____

_____

_____

_____

_____

_____

_____

**13**   What is a "want" I have defined as a "need"? Am I willing to turn it over to HP?

_____

_____

_____

_____

_____

_____

_____

_____

_____

_____

_____

_____

**14**   Do I equate thin with happy, or do I also recognize the importance of emotional and spiritual recovery? What brings me happiness today?

_____

_____

_____

_____

_____

_____

_____

_____

_____

_____

_____

**15**  Do I behave as though I can save myself from my disease? How do I accept my Higher Power's help?

_____

_____

_____

_____

_____

_____

_____

_____

_____

_____

_____

**16**  What are some examples of how I'm living in joy and gratitude?

_____

_____

_____

_____

_____

_____

_____

_____

_____

_____

**17** Can I describe a situation where I may not have *wanted* to do something but have become *willing* to do it?

_____

_____

_____

_____

_____

_____

_____

_____

_____

_____

_____

**18** What are 10 or more things for which I am grateful?

_____

_____

_____

_____

_____

_____

_____

_____

_____

_____

_____

**19** How would I describe three instances where I have been willing to change, and one situation where I am not yet willing?

_____

_____

_____

_____

_____

_____

_____

_____

_____

_____

_____

_____

**20** Have I truly put down the fork? Am I willing to get honest about my food? What actions can I take?

_____

_____

_____

_____

_____

_____

_____

_____

_____

_____

_____

**21** What is my definition of humility? How does humility free me from the bondage of self?

_____

_____

_____

_____

_____

_____

_____

_____

_____

**22** What is my food plan, in detail? Is it working for me? Am I willing to review it with my sponsor? Why or why not?

_____

_____

_____

_____

_____

_____

_____

_____

**23** Does my concept and relationship with my Higher Power allow me to say anything at anytime to HP? If not, why not?

_____

_____

_____

_____

_____

_____

_____

_____

_____

_____

_____

**24** Have I made use of the tools that have helped others in OA? If not, what am I willing to do for recovery?

_____

_____

_____

_____

_____

_____

_____

_____

_____

_____

**25** How would I describe situations where I still struggle to maintain control, handle it, or do it myself? Am I willing to discuss this with a sponsor and ask for my Higher Power's help and guidance?

_____

_____

_____

_____

_____

_____

_____

_____

_____

_____

_____

**26** Do I eat my meals in a pleasant, unhurried way, or do I need to improve the quality of the time I spend at my meals? How could I do that?

_____

_____

_____

_____

_____

_____

_____

_____

_____

_____

**27** What defects of character are blocking me from spiritual growth, and what am I doing about them?

_____

_____

_____

_____

_____

_____

_____

_____

_____

_____

_____

**28** What do I do to support abstinence as my highest priority?

_____

_____

_____

_____

_____

_____

_____

_____

_____

_____

**29**   How would I describe a situation where I have heard my Higher Power's guidance?

_____

_____

_____

_____

_____

_____

_____

_____

_____

_____

_____

**30**   What are some examples of how I am living by the decision I made in the Third Step?

_____

_____

_____

_____

_____

_____

_____

_____

_____

_____

_____

# OCTOBER

1  What fears might be blocking me from relying on my Higher Power?
   What other stumbling blocks are in my way?

_____

_____

_____

_____

_____

_____

_____

_____

_____

_____

2  How has the clarity of abstinence helped me face situations that once
   seemed impossible?

_____

_____

_____

_____

_____

_____

_____

_____

_____

**3**    What are some areas in which, with God's guidance, I am taking action for my recovery?

_____

_____

_____

_____

_____

_____

_____

_____

_____

_____

**4**    In addition to release from food thoughts, what other areas of my life are benefitting from abstinence?

_____

_____

_____

_____

_____

_____

_____

_____

_____

**5** What areas of my life am I trying to control, and what steps can I take to turn them over to my Higher Power?

_____

_____

_____

_____

_____

_____

_____

_____

_____

_____

**6** How has my personality improved since I have become abstinent?

_____

_____

_____

_____

_____

_____

_____

_____

_____

**7** What wonderful character assets are replacing my defects as I practice Steps Six and Seven?

_____

_____

_____

_____

_____

_____

_____

_____

_____

_____

_____

**8** Do I still sometimes think I am in charge? What tools can I use to help when my life seems out of control?

_____

_____

_____

_____

_____

_____

_____

_____

_____

_____

**9** How might I express exuberance in my life today?

_____
_____
_____
_____
_____
_____
_____
_____
_____
_____

**10** How am I giving service today? How do I feel about this service?
What do I get from doing service?

_____
_____
_____
_____
_____
_____
_____
_____
_____

**11**    What am I doing today to strengthen the habit of abstinence?

_____

_____

_____

_____

_____

_____

_____

_____

_____

_____

_____

**12**    What potential, which my compulsive overeating blocked, am I discovering in my life?

_____

_____

_____

_____

_____

_____

_____

_____

_____

_____

**13**    How can I use the tool of writing to improve my connection with my Higher Power?

_____

_____

_____

_____

_____

_____

_____

_____

_____

_____

_____

**14**    Do I meditate? If so, what is my meditation practice? How can meditation benefit me?

_____

_____

_____

_____

_____

_____

_____

_____

_____

_____

**15**  What "old ways" am I hanging onto that may shortchange my opportunity for a new way of life?

_____

_____

_____

_____

_____

_____

_____

_____

_____

_____

_____

**16**  How has my description of a Higher Power defined my prayer life and reliance on God?

_____

_____

_____

_____

_____

_____

_____

_____

_____

_____

_____

**17** How is being present in my body helping me to be more aware of circumstances and feelings?

_____

_____

_____

_____

_____

_____

_____

_____

_____

_____

**18** What does "going to any length" mean for me?

_____

_____

_____

_____

_____

_____

_____

_____

_____

_____

**19** What are the people who have gone before me in OA showing me? What am I showing others?

_____

_____

_____

_____

_____

_____

_____

_____

_____

_____

_____

**20** How do I practice the slogan "Live and Let Live"? Am I truly aware and accepting that we all have our own path to follow?

_____

_____

_____

_____

_____

_____

_____

_____

_____

_____

**21**     What gifts from my experience will I share with a newcomer?

_____

_____

_____

_____

_____

_____

_____

_____

_____

_____

_____

**22**     Can I appreciate my past experiences but actually live in today?
How has the past contributed to the richness of who I have become?

_____

_____

_____

_____

_____

_____

_____

_____

_____

_____

**23** Do I still think I know what others should be doing or am I keeping the focus on my own recovery? How do I explain my answer?

_____

_____

_____

_____

_____

_____

_____

_____

_____

_____

_____

**24** Am I willing to change? How have the Steps contributed to my physical, emotional, and spiritual health?

_____

_____

_____

_____

_____

_____

_____

_____

_____

_____

**25** Do I listen for commonalities and not differences when others in OA share? When has someone's sharing helped me recognize my own behaviors that may need to be changed?

_____

_____

_____

_____

_____

_____

_____

_____

_____

_____

_____

**26** When have I "acted myself into a new way of thinking"? How might abstinence help to get rid of fear?

_____

_____

_____

_____

_____

_____

_____

_____

_____

_____

_____

**27**    Why would being too smart be a liability in my OA program? If I think I already know, am I teachable?

_____

_____

_____

_____

_____

_____

_____

_____

_____

_____

_____

_____

**28**    Where am I out of balance today? What action that leads to greater serenity has my Higher Power guided me to see?

_____

_____

_____

_____

_____

_____

_____

_____

_____

_____

_____

_____

**29**  What action do I take when I become conscious of fear's presence?

_____
_____
_____
_____
_____
_____
_____
_____
_____
_____
_____
_____

**30**  What shortcomings am I ready and willing to allow God to remove?

_____
_____
_____
_____
_____
_____
_____
_____
_____
_____
_____
_____

**31** How will I humbly allow my Higher Power to do what I could never do alone?

_____

_____

_____

_____

_____

_____

_____

_____

_____

_____

_____

_____

_____

_____

_____

_____

_____

_____

_____

_____

_____

_____

_____

_____

_____

_____

# NOVEMBER

**1** How do I seek conscious contact with my Higher Power? Can I describe a situation where I let go of my will?

---
---
---
---
---
---
---
---
---
---
---

**2** Do I allow external forces to determine my serenity? What makes me truly peaceful and happy?

---
---
---
---
---
---
---
---
---
---
---

**3**    Over what am I powerless? Do I act irresponsibly and call it powerlessness? For what am I responsible?

_____

_____

_____

_____

_____

_____

_____

_____

_____

_____

**4**    Do I make an effort to listen to that inner voice, that intuitive thought? What is a message I feel I received from HP?

_____

_____

_____

_____

_____

_____

_____

_____

_____

**5** | What does surrender mean to me? What gets in the way of my relationship with God?

_____

_____

_____

_____

_____

_____

_____

_____

_____

_____

**6** | Am I generous in sharing my recovery? Am I an example of spiritual, physical, and emotional healing? In what other ways can I help the suffering compulsive eater?

_____

_____

_____

_____

_____

_____

_____

_____

_____

_____

**7**   What surprises have I experienced in OA?

_____
_____
_____
_____
_____
_____
_____
_____
_____
_____
_____
_____

**8**   How does my Higher Power speak to me? Am I paying attention?

_____
_____
_____
_____
_____
_____
_____
_____
_____
_____

**9** In what ways do I isolate from others? What other behaviors do me harm?

_____
_____
_____
_____
_____
_____
_____
_____
_____
_____
_____
_____

**10** Have I ever experienced a sense of separation from HP and others? Can I act as if this program will work whether or not I believe it? Why or why not?

_____
_____
_____
_____
_____
_____
_____
_____
_____
_____
_____

**11** Have I become complacent about the daily activities that support my abstinence and my spiritual and emotional recovery? Is there any tool I used in the beginning that I no longer use? If so, why?

_____

_____

_____

_____

_____

_____

_____

_____

_____

_____

_____

**12** Can I trust God to take care of me in *all* ways? If so, what are some examples? If not, what is standing in the way of that trust?

_____

_____

_____

_____

_____

_____

_____

_____

_____

_____

**13**   For what am I praying? Do I still give God instructions? Am I willing to trust?

_____

_____

_____

_____

_____

_____

_____

_____

_____

_____

_____

**14**   When do I put principles before personalities? Can I describe a time when I let a personality compromise my principles?

_____

_____

_____

_____

_____

_____

_____

_____

_____

_____

_____

_____

**15** Am I the best example of OA I can be? Would I attract a suffering compulsive eater to OA? If I'm not sure, what changes can I make?

_____
_____
_____
_____
_____
_____
_____
_____
_____
_____
_____

**16** Have I found sanity and abstinence working the Twelve Steps? If so, what must I do to maintain these precious gifts? If not, can I do more to work this program?

_____
_____
_____
_____
_____
_____
_____
_____
_____
_____

**17** What does humility mean to me?

_____
_____
_____
_____
_____
_____
_____
_____
_____
_____
_____

**18** Are the legs of equal size on my recovery's three-legged stool?
If one of the legs is short, what can I do to help?

_____
_____
_____
_____
_____
_____
_____
_____
_____
_____

**19**  Do I persist in trying to "fix" myself, by myself? What is mine to do, and what do I give to my HP?

_____
_____
_____
_____
_____
_____
_____
_____
_____
_____
_____
_____

**20**  When has another OA member's experience, strength, and hope lifted me up? What does the OA Fellowship mean to me?

_____
_____
_____
_____
_____
_____
_____
_____
_____
_____
_____

**21**  How will ongoing abstinence improve my life?

_____
_____
_____
_____
_____
_____
_____
_____
_____
_____
_____
_____
_____

**22**  Am I willing to assume a physical posture of humility when I pray? If not, why not? What might this mean in my relationship with my Higher Power?

_____
_____
_____
_____
_____
_____
_____
_____
_____
_____
_____

**23** What type of service am I doing in the OA Fellowship? What have been the benefits? If I am not giving service, why not?

_____
_____
_____
_____
_____
_____
_____
_____
_____
_____
_____
_____

**24** Do I pick up an OA tool when food thoughts come? If I don't take an action OA suggests, what happens? Which tools do I use during these times?

_____
_____
_____
_____
_____
_____
_____
_____
_____
_____
_____

**25** Do I cling to fear and indecision in any areas of my life? How can I increase my trust in my Higher Power?

_____
_____
_____
_____
_____
_____
_____
_____
_____
_____
_____
_____

**26** Am I being responsible for myself in all areas of my life? How am I self-supporting in my relationships, work, obligations, and recovery?

_____
_____
_____
_____
_____
_____
_____
_____
_____
_____
_____

**27** How do I handle special events (many of which center around food)? How have I or have I not used the OA tools during one of these events, and how did it turn out?

_____

_____

_____

_____

_____

_____

_____

_____

_____

_____

**28** What does my spiritual practice include? Do I always make time for my spiritual well-being? If not, why not?

_____

_____

_____

_____

_____

_____

_____

_____

_____

_____

**29**     How has this program helped me to mature in my relationships with others and with God?

_____

_____

_____

_____

_____

_____

_____

_____

_____

_____

_____

_____

**30**     What actions do I take throughout the day to align myself with my Higher Power? How do I feel when I am at odds with the God of my understanding?

_____

_____

_____

_____

_____

_____

_____

_____

_____

_____

_____

# DECEMBER

**1** Each of the Twelve Steps gives us a gift. What spiritual gift have I received as a result of my work on the Steps?

_____

_____

_____

_____

_____

_____

_____

_____

_____

_____

_____

_____

**2** What fear has been bothering me? What actions am I willing to take?

_____

_____

_____

_____

_____

_____

_____

_____

_____

_____

**3**     What is something I cannot change that God is helping me to accept? What is something I can change, and what actions would I like to take?

_____

_____

_____

_____

_____

_____

_____

_____

_____

_____

_____

**4**     Can I write a letter to God, holding nothing back? How does writing that letter make me feel?

_____

_____

_____

_____

_____

_____

_____

_____

_____

_____

**5** Do I have difficulty with the word "trust"? What footwork must I still do? Am I willing to trust my Higher Power with the *result*?

_____

_____

_____

_____

_____

_____

_____

_____

_____

_____

_____

_____

**6** How has the fellowship aspect of this program (meetings, telephone, sponsorship) helped me with my recovery?

_____

_____

_____

_____

_____

_____

_____

_____

_____

_____

**7**  Which of the five P's (practice, prayer, perseverance, patience, and progress) resonates with me right now? Would I like that word to be my mantra for today?

_____

_____

_____

_____

_____

_____

_____

_____

_____

_____

_____

**8**  How would I describe my true desire to stop eating compulsively? How could "acting as if" help me in difficult times?

_____

_____

_____

_____

_____

_____

_____

_____

_____

_____

**9**  Do I begin each day with prayer and meditation, or do I rush into my day thinking I don't have time? How has my morning routine changed since I joined OA?

_____

_____

_____

_____

_____

_____

_____

_____

_____

_____

_____

_____

**10**  Do I have feelings of jealousy, shame, and rage? What actions can I take to move into acceptance?

_____

_____

_____

_____

_____

_____

_____

_____

_____

_____

**11** Is my recovery a journey or a destination? Why?

_____

_____

_____

_____

_____

_____

_____

_____

_____

_____

_____

**12** Do I share when I feel complacent, or do I isolate? What steps can I take to trust enough to share about it?

_____

_____

_____

_____

_____

_____

_____

_____

_____

_____

**13**  Besides working the Twelve Steps and asking for God's help, what other actions can help me make good food decisions and overcome "food fears"?

_____

_____

_____

_____

_____

_____

_____

_____

_____

_____

_____

_____

_____

_____

_____

**14**  What would I include on a list of qualities I'd like to practice "acting as if"? For instance: "I'd like to act as if I'm a patient person." Have I had any awakenings as a result of "acting as if"? If so, what were those awakenings?

_____

_____

_____

_____

_____

_____

_____

_____

_____

_____

_____

_____

**15** When writing, do I have a problem identifying my feelings? Who or what can help me?

_____

_____

_____

_____

_____

_____

_____

_____

_____

_____

_____

**16** What can I do to keep my program simple? Do I ask for my HP's help daily? If not, why?

_____

_____

_____

_____

_____

_____

_____

_____

_____

_____

**17**    Do I share my experience, strength, and hope with others, or do I lecture? What actions of mine carry the OA message?

_____

_____

_____

_____

_____

_____

_____

_____

_____

_____

_____

_____

**18**    When have I experienced gray, bleak days? What helped me most at the time? Did I consult my Higher Power?

_____

_____

_____

_____

_____

_____

_____

_____

_____

_____

_____

**19** Can I write a letter to God acknowledging my willingness (or need for willingness) to follow Good Orderly Direction? How am I willing to go to any lengths to recover?

_____

_____

_____

_____

_____

_____

_____

_____

_____

_____

_____

_____

**20** How do I feel when I follow my food plan? Do I need other people's approval for what I eat?

_____

_____

_____

_____

_____

_____

_____

_____

_____

_____

_____

**21**    How has doing service improved my recovery?

_____

_____

_____

_____

_____

_____

_____

_____

_____

_____

_____

_____

**22**    Have I been denying the truth about this disease and myself?
What spiritual gift have I received as a result of my honesty?

_____

_____

_____

_____

_____

_____

_____

_____

_____

_____

_____

**23** What have I learned about myself by doing service?

_____
_____
_____
_____
_____
_____
_____
_____
_____
_____
_____

**24** What payoff did compulsive overeating give me? What has the OA program given me besides weight change?

_____
_____
_____
_____
_____
_____
_____
_____
_____
_____
_____

**25** Have I found the peace of "letting go" of the committee in my head? What does that feel like?

_____

_____

_____

_____

_____

_____

_____

_____

_____

_____

_____

_____

**26** Which OA promises have come true for me thus far? Am I continuing to work the Steps, use the tools and stay in the solution?

_____

_____

_____

_____

_____

_____

_____

_____

_____

_____

_____

**27** Can I see myself as no better and no worse than my fellows? Have I found comfort in anonymity?  How do I explain my responses?

_____

_____

_____

_____

_____

_____

_____

_____

_____

_____

_____

**28** Someone defined "intimacy" as "into me see." How have I been able to look inside myself with my Higher Power's help?

_____

_____

_____

_____

_____

_____

_____

_____

_____

_____

_____

**29**     Do I say "yes" to others too quickly and too often? Am I a caregiver who neglects caring for myself? How can I balance caring for others with caring for myself?

_____
_____
_____
_____
_____
_____
_____
_____
_____
_____
_____

**30**     What would I include on a list of the things I wish I could change but know I can't change? What would I include on a list of the things I can change but have been procrastinating because I'm afraid?

_____
_____
_____
_____
_____
_____
_____
_____
_____

What would I include on a gratitude list of all the gifts OA has given me?

_____

_____

_____

_____

_____

_____

_____

_____

_____

_____

_____

_____

_____

_____

_____

_____

_____

_____

_____

_____

_____

_____

_____

_____

_____

_____

1.  We admitted we were powerless over food — that our lives had become unmanageable.

2.  Came to believe that a Power greater than ourselves could restore us to sanity.

3.  Made a decision to turn our will and our lives over to the care of God *as we understood Him.*

4.  Made a searching and fearless moral inventory of ourselves.

5.  Admitted to God, to ourselves and to another human being the exact nature of our wrongs.

6.  Were entirely ready to have God remove all these defects of character.

7.  Humbly asked Him to remove our shortcomings.

8.  Made a list of all persons we had harmed and became willing to make amends to them all.

9.  Made direct amends to such people wherever possible, except when to do so would injure them or others.

10. Continued to take personal inventory and when we were wrong, promptly admitted it.

11. Sought through prayer and meditation to improve our conscious contact with God *as we understood Him,* praying only for knowledge of His will for us and the power to carry that out.

12. Having had a spiritual awakening as the result of these Steps, we tried to carry this message to compulsive overeaters and to practice these principles in all our affairs.

Permission to use the Twelve Steps of Alcoholics Anonymous for adaptation granted by AA World Services, Inc.

# The Twelve Traditions of Overeaters Anonymous

1. Our common welfare should come first; personal recovery depends upon OA unity.

2. For our group purpose there is but one ultimate authority — a loving God as He may express Himself in our group conscience. Our leaders are but trusted servants; they do not govern.

3. The only requirement for OA membership is a desire to stop eating compulsively.

4. Each group should be autonomous except in matters affecting other groups or OA as a whole.

5. Each group has but one primary purpose — to carry its message to the compulsive overeater who still suffers.

6. An OA group ought never endorse, finance or lend the OA name to any related facility or outside enterprise, lest problems of money, property and prestige divert us from our primary purpose.

7. Every OA group ought to be fully self-supporting, declining outside contributions.

8. Overeaters Anonymous should remain forever non-professional, but our service centers may employ special workers.

9. OA, as such, ought never be organized; but we may create service boards or committees directly responsible to those they serve.

10. Overeaters Anonymous has no opinion on outside issues; hence the OA name ought never be drawn into public controversy.

11. Our public relations policy is based on attraction rather than promotion; we need always maintain personal anonymity at the level of press, radio, films, television and other public media of communication.

12. Anonymity is the spiritual foundation of all these Traditions, ever reminding us to place principles before personalities.

Permission to use the Twelve Traditions of Alcoholics Anonymous for adaptation granted by AA World Services, Inc

For more information on Overeaters Anonymous, write to
the World Service Office, PO Box 44020,
Rio Rancho, NM 87174-4020 USA.

Or visit our Web site at www.oa.org

# NOTES

# NOTES